Year 1 - Independent Writin

C000199337

Introduction

This book of 'Independent Writing Activities' covers the genres for the 5 to 6 year old age group. It has been written to the UK National Strategy Primary Framework for Literacy.

It contains at least two independent writing activities for each genre type and is an ideal vehicle for assessing pupil progress in writing when used with the different Levels found in the Writing Assessment Guidelines, which accompany the Primary Framework for Literacy. (The appropriate levels for this age group have been reproduced under licence at the beginning of this book.)

The author has also used this approach successfully with children to embed the features of each genre. This was achieved by re-visiting a previously studied genre later in the term, so that the children practised it once again. This ensured that the features of that particular type of writing remained firmly embedded in the children's memory. Thus when the children were tested or came to write in that particular genre at a later date it was not just a distant memory.

There are six similar books in this series covering the work of pupils from Year 1 through to Year 6 (ages 5 to 11). PDF or Download versions are also available of these books for use on Interactive Whiteboards.

Index

Topical Resources publishes a range of Educational Materials for use in Primary Schools and Pre-School Nurseries and Playgroups.

Copyright © 2009 Heather Bell
First Published September 2009.
ISBN: 978-1-907269-05-9

Illustrated by John Hutchinson, Art Works, Fairhaven, 69 Worden Lane, Leyland, Preston

Designed by Paul Sealey, PS3 Creative, 3 Wentworth Drive, Thornton, Lancashire.

Printed in the UK for 'Topical Resources' by T. Snape and Co Ltd., Boltons Court, Preston, Lancashire.

For the latest catalogue
Tel 01772 863158
Fax 01772 866153
email: sales@topical-resources.co.uk

Visit our Website at:
www.topical-resources.co.uk

Writing assessment guidelines: levels 1 and 2

Pupil name   Class/Group   Date

	AF5 – vary sentences for clarity, purpose and effect	AF6 – write with technical accuracy of syntax and punctuation in phrases, clauses and sentences	AF3 – organise and present whole texts effectively, sequencing and structuring information, ideas and events	AF4 – construct paragraphs and use cohesion within and between paragraphs	AF1 – write imaginative, interesting and thoughtful texts	AF2 – produce texts which are appropriate to task, reader and purpose	AF7 – select appropriate and effective vocabulary	AF8 – use correct spelling	Handwriting and presentation
Level 2	In some forms of writing: ■ some variation in sentence openings, e.g. *not always starting with name or pronoun* ■ mainly simple sentences with *and* used to connect clauses ■ past and present tense generally consistent	In some forms of writing: ■ clause structure mostly grammatically correct ■ sentence demarcation with capital letters and full stops usually accurate ■ some accurate use of question and exclamation marks, and commas in lists	In some forms of writing: ■ some basic sequencing of ideas or material, e.g. *time-related words or phrases, line breaks, headings, numbers* ■ openings and/or closings sometimes signalled	In some forms of writing: ■ ideas in sections grouped by content, some linking by simple pronouns	In some forms of writing: ■ mostly relevant ideas and content, sometimes repetitive or sparse ■ some apt word choices create interest ■ brief comments, questions about events or actions suggest viewpoint	In some forms of writing: ■ some basic purpose established, e.g. *main features of story, report* ■ some appropriate features of the given form used ■ some attempts to adopt appropriate style	In some forms of writing: ■ simple, often speech-like vocabulary conveys relevant meanings ■ some adventurous word choices, e.g. *opportune use of new vocabulary*	In some forms of writing: ■ usually correct spelling of: ○ high frequency grammatical function words ○ common single-morpheme content/lexical words ■ likely errors: ○ inflected endings, e.g. *past tense, plurals, adverbs* ○ phonetic attempts at vowel digraphs	In some forms of writing: ■ letters generally correctly shaped but inconsistencies in orientation, size and use of upper/lower case letters ■ clear letter formation, with ascenders and descenders distinguished, generally upper and lower case letters not mixed within words
Level 1	In some writing, usually with support: ■ reliance on simple phrases and clauses ■ some sentence-like structures formed by chaining clauses together, e.g. *series of ideas joined by repeated use of 'and'*	In some writing, usually with support: ■ mostly grammatically accurate clauses ■ some awareness of use of full stops and capital letters, e.g. *beginning/end of sentence*	In some writing, usually with support: ■ some formulaic phrases indicate start/end of text, e.g. *once upon a time, one day, the end* ■ events/ideas sometimes in appropriate order, e.g. *actions listed in time sequence, items numbered*	In some writing, usually with support: ■ simple connections between ideas, events, e.g. *repeated nouns, pronouns relate to main idea*	In some writing, usually with support: ■ basic information and ideas conveyed through appropriate word choice, e.g. *relate to topic* ■ some descriptive language, e.g. *colour, size, simple emotion*	In some writing, usually with support: ■ some indication of basic purpose, particular form or awareness of reader, e.g. *story, label, message*	In some writing, usually with support: ■ mostly simple vocabulary ■ communicates meaning through repetition of key words	In some writing, usually with support: ■ usually correct spelling of simple high-frequency words ■ phonetically plausible attempts at words with digraphs and double letters ■ sufficient number of recognisable words for writing to be readable, including, e.g. *use of letter names to approximate syllables and words*	In some writing, usually with support: ■ most letters correctly formed and orientated ■ spaces between words ■ upper and lower case sometimes distinguished ■ use of ICT, e.g. *use keyboard to type own name*
BL									
IE									

Overall assessment (tick one box only)   Low 1   Secure 1   High 1   Low 2   Secure 2   High 2

QCA 00022-2009DWO-EN-01

Writing assessment guidelines: levels 2 and 3

Pupil name _____ Class/Group _____ Date _____

	AF5 – vary sentences for clarity, purpose and effect	AF6 – write with technical accuracy of syntax and punctuation in phrases, clauses and sentences	AF3 – organise and present whole texts effectively, sequencing and structuring information, ideas and events	AF4 – construct paragraphs and use cohesion within and between paragraphs	AF1 – write imaginative, interesting and thoughtful texts	AF2 – produce texts which are appropriate to task, reader and purpose	AF7 – select appropriate and effective vocabulary	AF8 – use correct spelling	Handwriting and presentation
Level 3	**In most writing** • reliance mainly on simply structured sentences, variation with support, e.g. *some complex sentences* • *and, but, so* are the most common connectives, subordination occasionally • some limited variation in use of tense and verb forms, not always secure	**In most writing** • straightforward sentences usually demarcated accurately with full stops, capital letters, question and exclamation marks • some, limited, use of speech punctuation • comma splicing evident, particularly in narrative	**In most writing** • some attempt to organise ideas with related points placed next to each other • openings and closings usually signalled • some attempt to sequence ideas or material logically	**In most writing** • some internal structure within sections of text *e.g. one-sentence paragraphs or ideas loosely organised* • within paragraphs/sections, some links between sentences, *e.g. use of pronouns or of adverbials* • movement between paragraphs/sections sometimes abrupt or disjointed	**In most writing** • some appropriate ideas and content included • some attempt to elaborate on basic information or events, *e.g. nouns expanded by simple adjectives* • attempt to adopt viewpoint, though often not maintained or inconsistent, *e.g. attitude expressed, but with little elaboration*	**In most writing** • purpose established at a general level • main features of selected form sometimes signalled to the reader • some attempts at appropriate style, with attention to reader	**In most writing** • simple, generally appropriate vocabulary used, limited in range • some words selected for effect or occasion	**In most writing** • correct spelling of some common grammatical function words common content/lexical words with more than one morpheme, including compound words • likely errors *some inflected endings, e.g. past tense, comparatives, adverbs some phonetically plausible attempts at content/lexical words*	**In most writing** • legible style, shows accurate and consistent letter formation, sometimes joined
Level 2	**In some forms of writing** • some variation in sentence openings, *e.g. not always starting with name or pronoun* • mainly simple sentences with *and* used to connect clauses • past and present tense generally consistent	**In some forms of writing** • clause structure mostly grammatically correct • sentence demarcation with capital letters and full stops usually accurate • some accurate use of question and exclamation marks, and commas in lists	**In some forms of writing** • some basic sequencing of ideas or material, *e.g. time-related words or phrases, line breaks, headings, numbers* • openings and/or closings sometimes signalled	**In some forms of writing** • ideas in sections grouped by content, some linking by simple pronouns	**In some forms of writing** • mostly relevant ideas and content, sometimes repetitive or sparse • some apt word choices create interest • brief comments, questions about events or actions suggest viewpoint	**In some forms of writing** • some basic purpose established, *e.g. main features of story, report* • some appropriate features of the given form used • some attempts to adopt appropriate style	**In some forms of writing** • simple, often speech-like vocabulary conveys relevant meanings • some adventurous word choices, *e.g. opportune use of new vocabulary*	**In some forms of writing** • usually correct spelling of high frequency grammatical function words common single morpheme content/lexical words • likely errors *inflected endings, e.g. past tense, plurals, adverbs phonetic attempts at vowel digraphs*	**In some forms of writing** • letters generally correctly shaped but inconsistencies in orientation, size and use of upper/lower case letters • clear letter formation, with ascenders and descenders distinguished, generally upper and lower case letters not mixed within words
BL									
IE									

Key: BL Below level   IE Insufficient evidence

Overall assessment (tick one box only)

Low 2	Secure 2	High 2	Low 3	Secure 3	High 3
☐	☐	☐	☐	☐	☐

Breakfast in Bed

Tom wanted to give his Mum a surprise by making her breakfast in bed. Look at the pictures to find out what happened.

Task

Your task is to write the story of what happened using the pictures to help you.

Name _____   Date _____

Breakfast in Bed

What happened in picture 1?

What happened in picture 2?

What happened in picture 3?

What happened in picture 4?

Name _____   Date _____

Breakfast in Bed

_____

_____

_____

_____

_____

_____

_____

_____

_____

_____

_____

_____

The Magical Bird

Here is a picture of an amazing magical bird, which can carry you anywhere you would like to go.

Task

Your task is to write a story telling where the bird takes you.

Name _____ Date _____

The Magical Bird

What does the magical bird look like?

Where do you go?

How do you feel?

How does your story end? How do you get home?

Name _____   Date _____

The Magical Bird

_____

_____

_____

_____

_____

_____

_____

_____

_____

_____

Goldilocks and the Three Bears

Look at the pictures in the story below.

Task

Your task is to write captions for the pictures.

Name _____   Date _____

Goldilocks and the Three Bears

Words about Goldilocks

Words about the Three Bears

Name _____   Date _____

Goldilocks and the Three Bears

1

_____

2

_____

3

_____

4

_____

5

_____

6

_____

Birthday Food

Tom and Sophie are having a birthday party. Look at the picture of some of the food they would like.

Task

Your task is to write the shopping list for the birthday food. Remember to include some things you really like.

Name _____ Date _____

Birthday Food

Draw and label some birthday foods.

Name _____   Date _____

My List of Birthday Food

_____

_____

_____

_____

_____

_____

_____

_____

_____

_____

My food pictures:

Toy Shop

It will soon be Fiona and John's birthdays. They look in the toyshop window. Look at what they see.

Task

Your task is to write a list of what either Fiona or John chooses for their birthday.

Name _____ Date _____

Toy Shop

Draw and label the things you would choose if you were either Fiona or John.

Name _____ **Date** _____

Toy Shop List

_____

_____

_____

_____

_____

_____

_____

_____

_____

My pictures of toys:

How to Plant a Bulb

Emma's class have planted some bulbs. Look at the pictures to find out what they did.

1

2

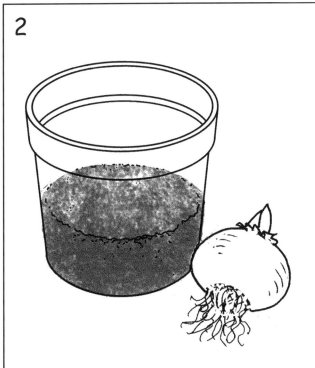

3

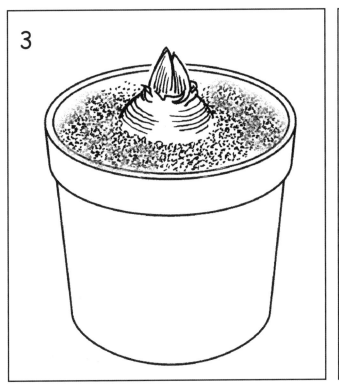

4

Task

Your task is to write the instructions for planting bulbs.

Name _____   Date _____

How to Plant a Bulb

Draw and label what you will need.

Name _____ **Date** _____

How to Plant a Bulb

List what you need:

_____

_____

_____

What you will need to do:

1. _____

_____

_____

_____

_____

_____

_____

_____

How to Make a Bowl of Cereal

John's mum was ill in bed. He had to make his own breakfast.

1

2

3

4

Task

Your task is to write the instructions for making a bowl of breakfast cereal.

Name _____   Date _____

How to Make a Bowl of Cereal

Draw and label what you will need.

Name _____   Date _____

How to Make a Bowl of Cereal

What you will need: _____

_____

_____

_____

What you will need to do: _____

1 _____

_____

2 _____

_____

3 _____

_____

4 _____

A Special Event

Last Tuesday a storyteller came to Sam's school.
This is what Sam wrote about the event.

Story Teller in School

Last Tuesday a storyteller came to school. He read us a funny story that he had written about a dog that was always getting into trouble. The best part was when he brought in his dog and I got to stroke it. I felt really happy.

Task

Your task is to write a recount of a special event that has happened in your school.

Name _____   **Date** _____

A Special Event

Title:

↓

What happened?

↓

The best part was ...

↓

How I felt ...

Name _____   Date _____

A Special Event

Title: _____

_____

_____

_____

_____

_____

_____

_____

_____

_____

_____

_____

The Day Out

Emily went on a special day out with her family. This is what she wrote about...

A Trip to the Fun Fair

On Saturday I went in the car to the Fun Fair.

I went with my family. I went on lots of rides.

I liked the Log Flume. We had tea in the café.

We went home when it got dark. The best part

was when I won a teddy.

Task

Your task is to write about a special day out you have had.

Name _____   Date _____

The Day Out

Title:

↓

How you got there:

↓

What you did:

↓

What you liked best:

↓

How you felt about it:

Name _____   **Date** _____

The Day Out

Your Title: _____

_____

_____

_____

_____

_____

_____

_____

_____

_____

Looking After a Pet

Here is some information Tom wrote about looking after his rabbit.

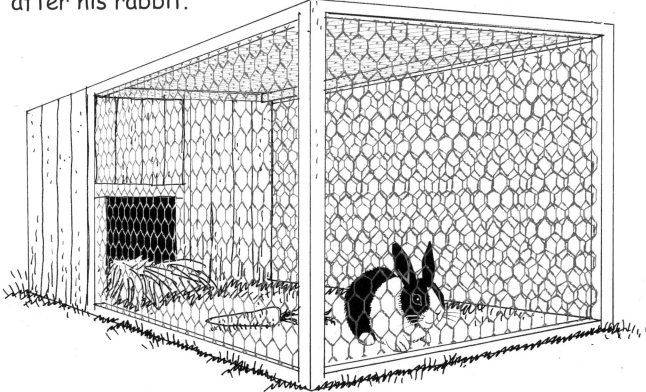

Looking After a Rabbit
Pet rabbits live in a hutch with a run.

They eat dried food and fresh vegetables. They need to be fed twice a day.

Their hutch must be cleaned out often and fresh straw put in. They must have fresh water to drink. This should be checked every day.

Rabbits need a large run in which to exercise and play.

Task

Your task is to write about looking after a pet.

Name _____ **Date** _____

Looking After a Pet

What kind of pet?

Where it lives...

_____

What it eats and drinks ...

_____

How to keep it clean ...

_____

The exercise it needs ...

_____

Drawing

Name _____ Date _____

Looking After a Pet

_____

_____

_____

_____

_____

_____

_____

_____

_____

_____

_____

Looking After My Body

Class 2 are learning about how to keep healthy.
This is what Billy wrote about looking after his body.

Looking After My Body

To stay well we need to eat healthy food like fruit, vegetables, meat, milk, eggs and cheese.

It is important to take exercise such as walking, swimming or riding a bike.

Keeping clean is also important. We must wash or shower often.

Our body also needs lots of sleep each night.

Task

Your task is to write about how to look after your teeth.

Name _____ Date _____

Looking After My Body

Title: Teeth

Why we need teeth...

_____

How to keep teeth clean...

_____

Foods which keep teeth healthy...

_____

Visiting the dentist...

_____

Picture of smiling face with lots of teeth...

Name _____　Date _____

Looking After My Body - Teeth

　© **Topical Resources.** May be photocopied for classroom use only.

Pattern Poems

Read the poem carefully.

Buzz, buzz, buzz went the bee
As she flew into the hive.

Bark, bark, bark went the dog
As he ran into his kennel.

Baa, baa, baa went the sheep
As it skipped into the field.

Task

Your task is to write a poem of your own with the same pattern as the one above. Write about other creatures and their homes.

Name _____   **Date** _____

Pattern Poems

Creature	Sound	Home

Name _____　**Date** _____

Pattern Poems

Buzz, buzz, buzz went the bee
As she flew into the hive.

Bark, bark, bark went the dog
As he ran into his kennel.

Baa, baa, baa went the sheep
As it skipped into the field.

_____

_____

_____

_____

_____

_____

More Pattern Poems

Here is a rhyming pattern poem. Read it carefully.

Five Little Mice

Five little mice played on the floor,
One hurt its leg and then there were four.

Four little mice slept under a tree,
One saw the cat and then there were three.

Three little mice hid in a shoe,
One found a piece of cheese and then there were two.

Two little mice having lots of fun,
One heard its mother shout and then there was one.

One little mouse felt too hot in the sun,
Ran back into its hole and then there were none.

Task

Your task is to write a poem of your own, with the same pattern as the one above, about five little cats.

Name _____   **Date** _____

More Pattern Poems

Words that rhyme with four...

Words that rhyme with three...

Words that rhyme with two...

Words that rhyme with one...

Words that rhyme with none...

Name _____   Date _____

More Pattern Poems

Five little cats sitting by the door,

One _____

_____ four.

Four little cats swimming in the sea,

One _____

_____ three.

Three little cats hiding in a shoe,

One _____

_____ two.

Two little cats _____ ,

One _____

_____ one.

One little cat _____ ,

_____

_____ none.